THE PIANO SOLOS OF
RICHARD · CLAYDERMAN
CHRISTMAS

AVE MARIA · 30
CHRISTMAS CONCERTO · 2
HANDEL'S LARGO · 7
JESU, JOY OF MAN'S DESIRING · 10
JINGLE BELLS · 20
THE LITTLE DRUMMER BOY · 24
ON CHRISTMAS NIGHT THE LIGHTS
ARE BURNING · 14
O TANNENBAUM MEDLEY · 33
SILENT NIGHT – HOLY NIGHT · 38
SILVER BELLS · 16

GW00643587

EXCLUSIVE DISTRIBUTORS:

MUSIC SALES LIMITED

8/9 FRITH STREET, LONDON, W1V 5TZ, ENGLAND

MUSIC SALES PTY. LIMITED

120 ROTHSCHILD AVENUE, ROSEBERY, NSW 2018, AUSTRALIA

THIS BOOK © COPYRIGHT 1986 BY WISE PUBLICATIONS
UK ISBN 0.7119.1091.X/UK Order No. AM 65194

ARRANGED BY FRANK BOOTH

MUSIC SALES' COMPLETE CATALOGUE LISTS THOUSANDS OF
TITLES AND IS FREE FROM YOUR LOCAL MUSIC SHOP, OR DIRECT FROM
MUSIC SALES LIMITED. PLEASE SEND A CHEQUE OR POSTAL ORDER FOR £1.50
FOR POSTAGE TO MUSIC SALES LIMITED, 8/9 FRITH STREET, LONDON W1V 5TZ.

UNAUTHORISED REPRODUCTION OF ANY PART OF
THIS PUBLICATION BY ANY MEANS INCLUDING PHOTOCOPYING IS
AN INFRINGEMENT OF COPYRIGHT.

PRINTED IN THE UNITED KINGDOM BY
J.B. OFFSET PRINTERS (MARKS TEY), MARKS TEY, ESSEX.

WISE PUBLICATIONS
LONDON/NEW YORK/SYDNEY

CHRISTMAS CONCERTO

COMPOSER: ARCANGELO CORELLI
ARRANGER: OLIVIER TOUSSAINT AND GERARD SALESSES

© COPYRIGHT 1983 DELPHINE EDITIONS FOR THE WORLD. ZOMBA MUSIC PUBLISHERS LTD.,
165 WILLESDEN HIGH ROAD, LONDON NW10 FOR THE UK AND EIRE.
ALL RIGHTS RESERVED. INTERNATIONAL COPYRIGHT SECURED.

3

Handel's Largo

COMPOSER: GEORGE FRIDERIC HANDEL
ARRANGER: OLIVIER TOUSSAINT AND GERARD SALESSES

© COPYRIGHT 1983 DELPHINE EDITIONS FOR THE WORLD. ZOMBA MUSIC PUBLISHERS LTD.,
165 WILLESDEN HIGH ROAD, LONDON NW10 FOR THE UK AND EIRE.
ALL RIGHTS RESERVED. INTERNATIONAL COPYRIGHT SECURED.

Jesu, Joy Of Man's Desiring

COMPOSER: JOHANN SEBASTIAN BACH
ARRANGER: OLIVIER TOUSSAINT AND GERARD SALESSES

© COPYRIGHT 1983 DELPHINE EDITIONS FOR THE WORLD. ZOMBA MUSIC PUBLISHERS LTD.,
165 WILLESDEN HIGH ROAD, LONDON NW10 FOR THE UK AND EIRE.
ALL RIGHTS RESERVED. INTERNATIONAL COPYRIGHT SECURED.

13

ON CHRISTMAS NIGHT THE LIGHTS ARE BURNING

TRADITIONAL
ARRANGER: OLIVIER TOUSSAINT AND GERARD SALESSES

© COPYRIGHT 1983 DELPHINE EDITIONS FOR THE WORLD. ZOMBA MUSIC PUBLISHERS LTD.,
165 WILLESDEN HIGH ROAD, LONDON NW10 FOR THE UK AND EIRE.
ALL RIGHTS RESERVED. INTERNATIONAL COPYRIGHT SECURED.

Silver Bells

WORDS & MUSIC: JAY LIVINGSTON AND RAY EVANS

Moderately with a beat

© COPYRIGHT 1950 PARAMOUNT MUSIC CORP., USA. CHAPPEL MUSIC LTD., 129 PARK STREET, LONDON W1.
ALL RIGHTS RESERVED. INTERNATIONAL COPYRIGHT SECURED.

Jingle Bells

TRADITIONAL
ARRANGER: OLIVIER TOUSSAINT AND GERARD SALESSES

© COPYRIGHT 1983 DELPHINE EDITIONS FOR THE WORLD. ZOMBA MUSIC PUBLISHERS LTD.,
165 WILLESDEN HIGH ROAD, LONDON NW10 FOR THE UK AND EIRE.
ALL RIGHTS RESERVED. INTERNATIONAL COPYRIGHT SECURED.

23

The Little Drummer Boy

WORDS & MUSIC: HARRY SIMEONE, HENRY V. ONORATI AND KATHERINE K. DAVIS

© COPYRIGHT 1958 MILLS MUSIC INC. AND DELAWARE MUSIC CORP., USA.
CHAPPELL MUSIC LTD., 129 PARK STREET, LONDON W1.
ALL RIGHTS RESERVED. INTERNATIONAL COPYRIGHT SECURED.

29

Ave Maria

COMPOSER: FRANZ SCHUBERT
ARRANGER: OLIVIER TOUSSAINT AND GERARD SALESSES

© COPYRIGHT 1983 DELPHINE EDITIONS FOR THE WORLD. ZOMBA MUSIC PUBLISHERS LTD..
165 WILLESDEN HIGH ROAD, LONDON NW10 FOR THE UK AND EIRE.
ALL RIGHTS RESERVED. INTERNATIONAL COPYRIGHT SECURED.

O Tannenbaum Medley

TRADITIONAL
ARRANGER: OLIVIER TOUSSAINT AND GERARD SALESSES

© COPYRIGHT 1983 DELPHINE EDITIONS FOR THE WORLD. ZOMBA MUSIC PUBLISHERS LTD.,
165 WILLESDEN HIGH ROAD, LONDON NW10 FOR THE UK AND EIRE.
ALL RIGHTS RESERVED. INTERNATIONAL COPYRIGHT SECURED.

Silent Night–Holy Night

COMPOSER: GRUBER-MOHRE
ARRANGER: OLIVIER TOUSSAINT AND GERARD SALESSES

© COPYRIGHT 1983 DELPHINE EDITIONS FOR THE WORLD. ZOMBA MUSIC PUBLISHERS LTD..
165 WILLESDEN HIGH ROAD, LONDON NW10 FOR THE UK AND EIRE.
ALL RIGHTS RESERVED. INTERNATIONAL COPYRIGHT SECURED.

7/95 (22112)

7/95 (22112)